How
Do You
Say?

¿Cómo
se dice?

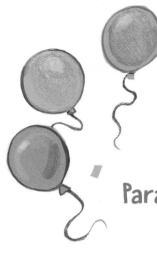

To friends, family, and dance parties
Para mis amigos, familiares y las fiestas de baile

Originally published by Henry Holt and Company as *How Do You Say / ¿Cómo se dice?*

Copyright © 2016 by Angela Dominguez

ISBN 978-1-338-12066-0

10 9 8 7 6 5 4 3 2 1   17 18 19 20 21

Printed in the U.S.A.   08
First Scholastic printing 2017

How Do You Say?
¿Cómo se dice?

Angela Dominguez

SCHOLASTIC INC.

Oooh

Food!

¡Buenos días!

Water

Agua

Happy

Feliz

Angela Dominguez writes and illustrates books for children, including *Maria Had a Little Llama*. She lives in New York City.

Angela Dominguez escribe e ilustra libros para niños, incluyendo *María tenía una llamita*. Ella vive en la ciudad de Nueva York.